Chemistry SL&HL

FOR THE IB DIPLOMA

Option D: Medicinal Chemistry

Martin Bluemel

PEAK

PEAK
STUDY RESOURCES

Published by:
Peak Study Resources Ltd
1 & 3 Kings Meadow
Oxford OX2 0DP
UK

www.peakib.com

Chemistry SL&HL Option D: Medicinal Chemistry
Study & Revision Guide for the IB Diploma

ISBN 978-1-913433-29-1

Peak Study & Revision Guides for the IB Diploma have been developed independently of the International Baccalaureate Organization (IBO). 'International Baccalaureate' and 'IB' are registered trademarks of the IBO.

Books may be ordered directly from the publisher (see www.peakib.com) and through online or local booksellers. For enquiries regarding titles, availability or retailers, please email books@peakib.com or use the form at www.peakib.com/contact.

Printed and bound in the UK
CPI Group (UK) Ltd, Croydon CR0 4YY
www.cpibooks.co.uk

MIX
Paper from
responsible sources
FSC® C013604

Cover image via Adobe Stock

The aim of Option D: Medicinal Chemistry is to give an understanding of the chemistry of some important molecules and procedures used in pharmaceutical medicine. There is also an attempt to raise awareness of some environmental implications of the substances involved.

This option involves the study of some large molecules. You are not required to memorise them, but you are expected to recognise functional groups and types of bonding within and between them. The structures of the most relevant molecules are given in section 37 of the IB *Chemistry Data Booklet*. You should also familiarise yourself with the relevant pages as part of your revision so that you can quickly find a structure you need in the exam.

Martin Bluemel

Acknowledgements

I am very grateful to the team at Peak (and at OSC who originally published this guide), and my wife, Jane, for her helpful comments. Thanks also to all my IB chemistry students, both at school and at OSC revision courses.

Image credits

Photographic images from Adobe Stock unless otherwise stated.

Figure 2.3: IR Spectrum of aspirin. Graph reproduced from NIST Chemistry WebBook

Figure 7.2: The 3D shape of the Taxol binding site. Adapted from Chellasamy, Selvaakumar and Mohammed, Sudheer M. M., 2014, 'An In silico Based Comparison of Drug Interactions in Wild and Mutant Human β-tubulin through Docking Studies', in *Avicenna Journal of Medical Biotechnology*, Vol. 6, (2), pp.81–93, fig. 4. https://www.ajmb.org/article?id=146 (accessed 14 March 2022)

Figure 7.5: Polarimeter. Based on Kaidor, via Wikimedia Commons, https://commons.wikimedia.org/wiki/File:Polarimeter_(Optical_rotation).svg (accessed 14 March 2022). Reproduced under the Creative Commons Attribution-Share Alike 3.0 Unported license.

Figure 8.1: MRI scan of the head. By Genesis12~enwiki at English Wikipedia, https://commons.wikimedia.org/wiki/File:Sagittal_brain_MRI.jpg (accessed 14 March 2022). Reproduced under Creative Commons Attribution-Share Alike 2.5 Generic license.

Figure 8.2: Tc-99m bone scan showing cancer in the bone. Konala, Praveen et al. "An Unusual Case of Persistent Groin Pain after Total Hip Arthroplasty: A Case Report." in *Journal of Medical Case Reports* 5 (2011): 67. PMC. Web. 7 Feb. 2018. Fig. 4. © 2011 Konala et al; licensee BioMed Central Ltd. Reproduced under CC BY 2.0.

Figure 9.5: The mass spectrum of a steroid. Smmudge, via Wikimedia Commons, https://commons.wikimedia.org/wiki/File:Mass_spectrum_brassicasterol.png (accessed 14 March 2022). Reproduced under CC-BY-SA-3.0.

Contents

Navigating the guide

This guide is structured to enable you to study efficiently:

- each topic forms a chapter;
- key terms are highlighted in bold;
- worked examples appear as a discrete section in the text;
- cross references provide links to the syllabus topics or between linked topics in this book; and
- practice questions appear at the end of each topic, with answers provided in the Appendix.

We use icons to help you quickly and easily identify different types of information.

Key to icons used in this study guide

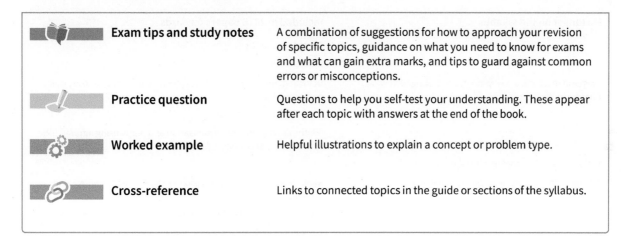

📖	**Exam tips and study notes**	A combination of suggestions for how to approach your revision of specific topics, guidance on what you need to know for exams and what can gain extra marks, and tips to guard against common errors or misconceptions.
✏️	**Practice question**	Questions to help you self-test your understanding. These appear after each topic with answers at the end of the book.
⚙️	**Worked example**	Helpful illustrations to explain a concept or problem type.
🔗	**Cross-reference**	Links to connected topics in the guide or sections of the syllabus.

Topics for SL and HL

SL students only have to cover some of the topics in this guide. These are sections **D1** to **D6** of the syllabus given in the IB's subject guide for Chemistry. The additional topics for HL are covered in sections **D7** to **D9**.

In this guide the topics are covered in syllabus order and the chapter numbers correspond to the syllabus sections. Therefore, the HL topics are covered at the end of the book and SL students do not have to read beyond this point.

Using IB Chemistry past papers

Past IB papers and their markschemes are a valuable aid to your revision. The more practice you get, the better your performance will be in the final exam. The following routine will help you make the best use of them.

1. Revise certain topics (or all topics if the exam is near).
2. Try to answer the questions on the topics you have revised in the same amount of time you would have in the exam (about **1.5 minutes per mark**) without looking at the markscheme.
3. Now use your class notes or this revision guide to look up and learn this missing material and improve/correct your answers.

4. Finally look at the markscheme and try to mark your answers as if you are the examiner. You may find that even though you now knew all the material, you still did not get full marks. If not, ask yourself 'why not?' Common reasons are:

    – you misunderstood what the question was asking for;
    – you did not write enough detail to get all the marks;
    – you did not use the right key words to get the mark(s).

If you are using *past papers from before May 2016*, then the questions will be *testing a different syllabus*. Previously, Option D was known as 'Medicines and Drugs'. Material has been deleted and new material added, including some that used to be in the Additional Higher Level (AHL) core. In particular, much of the previous topics on depressants, stimulants and mind-altering drugs have been replaced by drugs to control stomach acidity, environmental impact of drug wastes, nuclear medicine, and analysis and purification of drugs. The following table summarises the main changes.

No longer on the syllabus	Included in 2016 papers onwards
	Therapeutic index
	Bioavailability
Stages in research, development, and testing of new pharmaceutical products	Development of synthetic drugs (need, structure, synthesis, yield, and extraction)
	Drug-receptor interaction
	Synthesis of aspirin, recrystallisation and purity using infrared (IR) spectroscopy and melting point
Historical development of penicillin	
Alginates and anti-foaming agents in antacids	Ranitidine, omeprazole, and esomeprazole used to control acid secretion
	Calculation of pH of buffer solutions (was in AHL topic 19)
	Oseltamivir and zanamivir structures
	Active metabolites
Effects of depressants and alcohol abuse, diazepam, and fluoxetine structures	
Effects of stimulants, adrenaline, amphetamines, nicotine, and caffeine	
	Environmental impact (high and low level radioactive, solvents, and antibiotic waste)
	Green chemistry: e.g., Tamiflu
HL ONLY:	
Cisplatin and thalidomide as examples of stereoisomerism affecting drug action	Taxol (production and use)
	Use of a polarimeter (was in AHL topic 20)
Use of compound libraries and combinatorial chemistry in drug design	
	Nuclear medicine (radiotherapy, isotopes)
	Balancing nuclear equations
	Use of the nuclear half-life equation
	Targeted alpha therapy (TAT) and boron nuclear capture therapy (BNCT)
Mind-altering drugs (LSD, mescaline, psilocybin, and THC)	
Pros and cons for legalisation of cannabis	
	Use of IR, mass spectrometry (MS) and nuclear magnetic resonance (NMR) spectroscopy to determine an organic structure (was in Option A, and now also in AHL topic 21)
	Extraction and purification of an organic product, including fractional distillation
	Raoult's Law applied to organic extraction

Chapter 1: Pharmaceutical products and drug action

1.1 Drug action

A drug is a substance that has some kind of physiological effect when introduced into the body.

Most drugs act by interacting with some kind of receptor molecule in the body. Receptors are designed to detect the presence of specific molecules during the normal functioning of the body. These receptors will typically be large protein molecules which contain an active site where the small molecule can bind. The active site has a specific shape that only allows a very limited range of molecules to fit, depending on their shape. Drug molecules are often a similar shape and structure to the molecule that normally binds to the receptor.

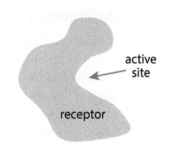

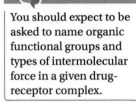

You should expect to be asked to name organic functional groups and types of intermolecular force in a given drug-receptor complex.

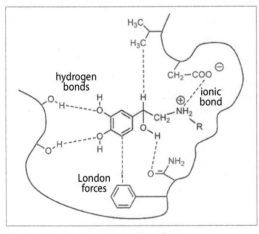

Figure 1.1: **Isoprenaline binding**

For example, the drug isoprenaline is used in the treatment of slow heart rate. It is shown in the figure opposite, binding to the active site of the receptor molecule that normally binds the hormone adrenaline (also called epinephrine), which naturally causes the heart rate to increase. Note how the shape of the active site ensures that particular functional groups are in the right position to allow the formation of various types of intermolecular force or ionic bonds between the receptor and the drug molecule.

See topic 4.4 of the core syllabus which covers the types of intermolecular forces.

1.2 Drug development

The development of a new synthetic drug includes three steps.

1. *Identifying the need*: typically, these are where current treatments for a condition are not as successful as required or available drugs have too many side effects and/or increasing problems with resistance (see page 11).

2. ***Identifying the possible structure*** of a new drug, by a number of approaches, including:

   – Computer analysis of the binding of natural molecules to the active site of the receptor molecule

   – Testing the drug activity of a range of possible molecules, firstly in vitro (outside the organism), then on animals, and finally on human volunteers.

3. ***Synthesis*** of the possible drug or ***extraction*** of the drug from a natural source with a high enough yield to make it commercially viable.

1.3   Drug dosage

1.3.1   Therapeutic index

Getting the right dosage of a drug is a balance between the amount needed for it to be effective, compared to the amounts of the drug that cause unacceptable adverse effects or, in extreme cases, lead to death. When a new drug is being developed, the toxicity of the drug must first be measured by giving it to animals (for example, rats) in steadily increasing doses. In these animal studies, two quantities are measured.

1.   The **minimum effective dose** (ED) needed to have the desired effect.

2.   The **lethal dose** (LD) that finally kills the animal.

Because individual animals are nonidentical, the quantities needed will vary from individual to individual, so the experiment must be done with a large population to average out the variation. The average amount is that needed for 50% of the population tested. Different drugs can be compared by defining the **therapeutic index** for the drug. Once a drug has passed the initial testing on animals, it can be tested on humans. However, for obvious ethical reasons, you cannot experimentally measure the lethal dose of the drug. Therefore, a **toxic dose** (TD) is identified, above which the adverse effects of the high dose are considered unacceptably high.

Note that these two different definitions of therapeutic index are similar, so take care to note the difference.

There are therefore two slightly different types of therapeutic index, depending on whether the studies have been carried out on animals or humans.

Type of therapeutic index	Definition in words	Expression
Animal studies	The **lethal dose** of a drug for 50% of the population (LD_{50}) divided by the **minimum effective dose** for 50% of the population (ED_{50}).	$\dfrac{LD_{50}}{ED_{50}}$
Human studies	The **toxic dose** of a drug for 50% of the population (TD_{50}) divided by the **minimum effective dose** for 50% of the population (ED_{50}).	$\dfrac{TD_{50}}{ED_{50}}$

The testing of drugs on animals to a lethal level is controversial because of ethical concerns over cruelty to the animals. However, in many countries the law requires these tests to be done before the drug can be tested on humans. Either way, both animal and human tests of potential new drugs are kept to a minimum for economic reasons as well as the ethical considerations, as they are expensive to carry out.

A drug that has a high therapeutic index is considered safe, as the effective dose is relatively small compared to the lethal or toxic dose. A drug with a low therapeutic index is likely to be rejected during the development stages, unless the potential medical benefits are extremely high and there are no alternatives available.

1.3.2 Therapeutic window

Once a drug is in use with patients, it is more useful to calculate the **therapeutic window** of the drug. This is the range of dosages between the minimum amounts of the drug that produce the desired effect and a medically unacceptable adverse effect. Drugs with a small therapeutic window must be used with careful monitoring by medical professionals, whereas drugs with a wide therapeutic window can be made more freely available, as the chances of the patient accidentally taking a toxic overdose are much lower.

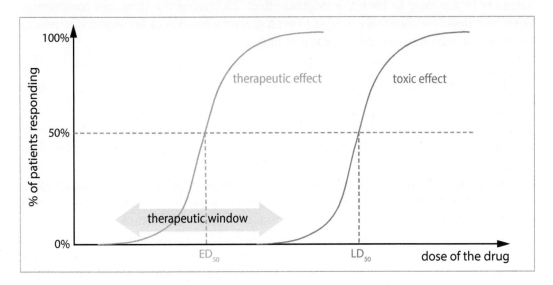

Figure 1.2: **Therapeutic window of a drug**

1.4 Drug administration

Drugs can be administered by a number of methods, including:

- Orally (pills or liquids)
- Rectally
- Injection (either into the bloodstream or into the muscle or below the skin)
- Inhalation
- Transdermally (skin patches or ointments).

The best method of administering a particular drug is decided by consideration of a number of factors, including whether the drug formulation is solid, liquid, or gas; how it can most effectively reach the part of the body where it is needed (see bioavailability below); how fast acting it needs to be; and how stable it is in different bodily environments.

1.4.1 Bioavailability

The bioavailability of a drug is the fraction of the administered dosage that reaches the target part of the human body. The bioavailability of a drug can be affected by a number of factors.

The method of administration: for example, injection directly into the affected tissue might improve the bioavailability compared to oral administration, where some of the drug might not be absorbed, or might get broken down by acid in the stomach.

The polarity of the drug, which depends on the functional groups on the drug molecule: for example, conversion of the polar carboxyl groups in morphine into less polar ester groups in heroin allows the molecules to cross the non-polar blood-brain barrier much more rapidly (see Chapter 3). Another example is the conversion of aspirin to its sodium salt to increase its aqueous solubility, which allows it to reach the stomach more rapidly (see Chapter 2).

1.4.2 Tolerance

The human body constantly adapts to any chemicals that it comes into contact with. Repeated use of a drug can result in tolerance, where the patient needs to take larger amounts of the drug to have the original effect. Increasing the dose can temporarily overcome tolerance, but this can lead to even greater tolerance or increased side effects along with a reduction in the therapeutic window.

1.4.3 Side effects

It is very common for drugs to affect not just the desired site of action, but also other processes in the human body. This can lead to side effects, in other words, adverse effects of drug effect other than that for which the drug was prescribed. During drug testing, all side effects are carefully monitored and the drug will not be approved unless the side effects are considered to be below an acceptable level in terms of frequency or seriousness. However, drugs used to treat more serious conditions, such as cancer, may be used even if side effects are greater if there is no other alternative. Patients should always be made aware of possible side effects before taking a drug, and these are typically listed with the information that comes with the drug. Occasionally a side effect might be beneficial: for example, aspirin taken as an analgesic also causes the thinning of the blood, which might be useful to prevent blood clots that cause heart attacks.

SERIOUS SIDE EFFECTS INCLUDE:	OTHER SIDE EFFECTS INCLUDE:
• Heart attack • Stroke • High blood pressure • Heart failure from body welling (fluid retention) • Kidney problems including kidney failure • Bleeding and ulcers in the stomach and intestine • Low red blood cells (anemia) • Life-threatening skins reactions • Life-threatening allergic reactions • Liver problems including liver failure • Asthma attacks in people who have asthma	• Stomach pain • Constipation • Diarrhea • Gas • Heartburn • Nausea • Vomiting • Dizziness

Figure 1.3: **An example of the side effects listed on drug packaging, in this case for Nabumetone, used to treat pain and swelling caused by arthritis**

1.4.4 Addiction

Tolerance can sometimes be confused with resistance and/or addiction. Make sure you know the precise definition of each term.

Some drugs can lead to addiction, where the patient becomes compulsive about taking the drug, despite possible adverse consequences. As the patient takes more of the drug as a result, this can lead to increased problems of tolerance and side effects. Examples of addictive drugs include: alcohol, nicotine, morphine, heroin and cocaine. Note that addiction is not the same as dependence, which is when unpleasant withdrawal symptoms occur if the drug is not taken. However drugs that lead to addiction often also lead to dependence.

1. Describe how therapeutic index is obtained in animal studies and also in human studies, and state two reasons why animal and human tests for drugs should be kept to a minimum. [4]

....

....

....

....

....

....

2. Explain the difference between tolerance and addiction. [2]

....

....

....

3. Explain what is meant by the term 'bioavailability' and describe two factors that can affect the bioavailability of a drug. [3]

....

....

....

....

4. Outline five main steps in the development of a synthetic drug. [5]

....

....

....

....

....

....

5.   Propofol is a drug commonly used as an anaesthetic and has the structure shown.

$(CH_3)_2CH$ —⬡— $CH(CH_3)_2$ with OH

Suggest two types of drug-receptor interaction you would expect to occur at the site of activity, and identify the functional groups involved.   [4]

....

....

....

....

....

Chapter 2:   Aspirin and Penicillin

2.1   Aspirin

Aspirin is a **mild analgesic**. Other common mild analgesics include paracetamol (also known as acetaminophen) and ibuprofen. Mild analgesics function by intercepting the pain stimulus at the source, often by interfering with the production of substances that cause the pain, swelling, or fever. This method of action is different from strong analgesics (see Chapter 3). The structures of aspirin, ibuprofen, and paracetamol are given in the *Chemistry Data Booklet*, published by the IBO.

Make sure you can identify all the functional groups in these three analgesics

aspirin   paracetamol   ibuprofen

Aspirin can also be used as an **anticoagulant**, which helps to prevent the formation of blood clots. The clotting of blood is a normal part of the body's mechanism to stop blood loss from a cut or wound. However, blood clots forming inside important blood vessels in the heart and brain can also lead to heart attacks and strokes. People at risk of heart attacks or strokes will often be prescribed a regular dose of aspirin as a **prophylactic**—in other words, as a preventative measure. Patients taking aspirin are advised not to drink alcohol. This is because aspirin has a **synergistic effect** with alcohol that can lead to bleeding in the stomach. A synergistic effect is an effect caused by the presence of both drugs that is greater than the sum of their individual effects.

2.1.1   Synthesis of aspirin

Aspirin is an ester formed by reaction of the hydroxyl group on salicylic acid with the carboxyl group of ethanoic acid. Like all esterification reactions, this reaction can be catalysed by concentrated sulfuric acid.

The synthesis of an ester from an alcohol and a carboxylic acid, which is an example of a condensation reaction, is introduced in core topic 10.2.

The direct reaction between ethanoic acid and salicylic acid does not give a particularly good yield, so in practice aspirin is usually made by reacting the salicylic acid with a much more reactive derivative of ethanoic acid, called **ethanoic anhydride**. This reaction produces more ethanoic acid as the by-product instead of water.

2.1.2 Laboratory preparation of aspirin

Aspirin can be prepared in the laboratory as outlined below.

1. Add a precisely weighed sample of salicylic acid crystals into a conical flask.

2. Slowly pour an excess of ethanoic anhydride on top of the crystals, mixing the reagents carefully (and taking great care not to breathe in the corrosive vapours of ethanoic acid formed). Leave the flask until the reaction is completed.

3. Add a little cold deionised water to the mixture to convert the excess ethanoic anhydride into ethanoic acid. The aspirin should crystallise out as a white solid as it is not very soluble in cold water. The ethanoic acid remains dissolved.

4. Filter the mixture by vacuum filtration, rinsing the aspirin crystals with a little more ice-cold water to wash off any remaining ethanoic acid.

2.1.3 Recrystallisation

The aspirin may still be contaminated with various other solid impurities. It can be purified by recrystallisation. This method can be used if the product is fairly soluble in hot solvent, but much less soluble in the solvent when cold. Possible solvents for aspirin include water, ethanol, or ethyl ethanoate.

1. Using hot ethanol, re-dissolve the aspirin in a beaker, using as little ethanol as possible to just dissolve it all.

2. Filter the solution using vacuum filtration—while it is still hot to remove any solid impurities mixed in with the crystals.

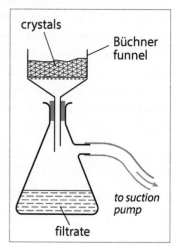

Figure 2.1: **Vacuum filtration**

3. Collect the filtrate in a flask and allow it to cool slowly in an ice-bath so that the aspirin crystallises out of the solution.

4. Filter the ice-cold mixture once again, this time keeping the residue of pure aspirin crystals. These can be left to dry to evaporate off the remaining ethanol.

The method of recrystallisation will inevitably result in a lower yield, as a little of the aspirin will remain dissolved, even in the cold ethanol. However, the product will be much purer, and it is usually worth the loss of yield.

2.1.4 Calculation of percentage yield

When it is dry, the aspirin can be weighed, and the percentage yield calculated by comparing the actual mass formed with the theoretical mass you should get from the mass of salicylic acid that was started with.

The calculation of percentage yields is first introduced in core topic 1.3.

A sample of aspirin was made using the method above, starting with 3.00 ±0.02 g of salicylic acid, ($C_7H_6O_3$), and an excess of ethanoic anhydride. The method produced 2.52 ±0.02 g of purified aspirin ($C_9H_8O_4$). Calculate the percentage yield, including its uncertainty.

Amount of salicylic acid used, $n = m/M_r$, = 3.00 g ÷ 138.13 g mol^{-1} = 0.0217 mol

Equation ratio = 1:1, so theoretical amount of aspirin produced = 0.0217 mol

Theoretical mass aspirin produced, $m = n \times M_r$

$$= 0.0217\,mol \times 180.17\,g\,mol^{-1} = 3.91\,g$$

Percentage yield of aspirin $\quad = 100 \times m_{actual}/m_{theoretical}$

$$= 100 \times 2.52 \div 3.91\,g = 64.4\%$$

Percentage uncertainty for the mass of salicylic acid = 100 × ±0.02 g ÷ 3.00 g = ±0.67%

Percentage uncertainty for the mass of aspirin = 100 × ±0.02 g ÷ 2.52 g = ±0.79%

Overall percentage uncertainty = 0.67% + 0.79% = ±1.46%, so absolute uncertainty = ±0.9%

2.1.5 Estimation of the purity of aspirin

The degree of purity of the aspirin produced can be investigated by melting point determination and/or infrared spectroscopy.

The **melting point** of aspirin is 138–140°C. If the aspirin is pure, then the solid crystals will be seen to melt sharply at this point when slowly heated in a narrow glass tube placed in a container of oil. Impurities will cause the solid to melt at a lower temperature and over a wider temperature range.

Comparison of the structure of aspirin with characteristic infrared absorptions given in section 26 of the *Chemistry*

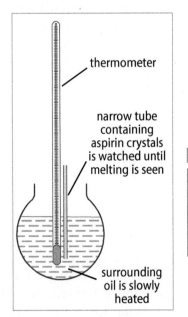

thermometer

narrow tube containing aspirin crystals is watched until melting is seen

surrounding oil is slowly heated

See core topic 11.3, which includes the use an infrared spectrum to identify the bonds in certain functional groups in the molecule.

Figure 2.2: **Melting point determination**

Data Booklet shows that the infrared spectrum of aspirin should contain peaks within the following ranges of wavenumbers:

- 1050–1410 cm^{-1} (due to the C–O in the ester group)
- 1700–1750 cm^{-1} (due to the C=O in the ester and carboxyl groups)
- 2500–3000 cm^{-1} (due to the O–H in the carboxyl group).

> The C–O peak is often hard to identify as a number of other peaks also occur in this region. It is easier to use the other two functional groups.

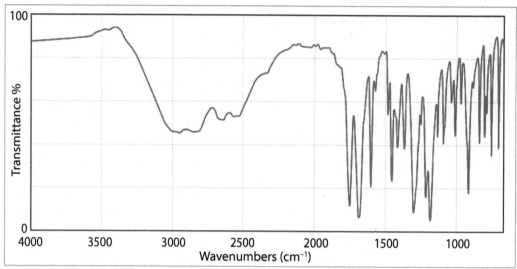

Figure 2.3: **IR spectrum of aspirin**
Source: NIST Chemistry WebBook

The presence of impurities would be indicated by other peaks appearing. For example, if the narrower OH peak at 3200–3600 cm^{-1} was present, this would indicate that some salicylic acid was still present, as this is a phenol. Computers can also compare the spectrum obtained with a database of spectra from pure aspirin and other possible impurities and estimate the % purity from the relative sizes of the peaks.

2.1.6 Soluble aspirin

Although aspirin has an OH group, which can hydrogen bond with water, the solubility of aspirin in water is quite low due to the large non-polar phenyl group. This can reduce its rate of dispersion when taken orally. Its aqueous solubility can be increased by neutralisation with a base, such as sodium hydroxide, to give its ionic sodium salt.

In a similar way, drugs containing the amino group –NH$_2$ can also be made more soluble by protonation to give –NH$_3^+$. For example, the antiviral drug oseltamivir (see Chapter 5) is commonly sold in its protonated form as either 'oseltamivir hydrochloride' or 'oseltamivir phosphate'. This is created by reaction of the basic amino group with a suitable acid.

oseltamivir   hydrochloric acid   oseltamivir hydrochloride

2.2   Penicillins

Penicillins are antibiotics naturally produced by fungi as part of their defence system against harmful bacteria. They have the core structure shown, with a side-chain that can vary. The general structure of penicillin is given in the *Chemistry Data Booklet*.

general structure of penicillin

2.2.1 Mechanism of action

A beta-lactam ring is a part of the core structure of penicillins. This four-membered ring is strained, because the normal bond angles of 120° and 109.5° on the three carbons and the nitrogen are reduced to 90°. This makes the carboxamide group in the ring particularly reactive. The ring opens up and reacts with the enzyme that is responsible for the formation of vital cross-links in the new bacterial cell walls that are being formed as the bacterium grows and divides. Therefore, the cell wall is weakened and becomes permeable to water. This leads to the bacteria taking in too much water by osmosis, causing the cells to burst and die.

2.2.2 Resistance to penicillins

Extensive use of penicillins since the 1940s has led to the evolution of bacteria which are resistant to the original penicillin isolated from fungi. These bacteria contain a **penicillinase** enzyme, which hydrolyses the reactive carboxamide group before it can react with the enzyme responsible for the cross-linking of the cell wall.

In an attempt to counter this resistance, other penicillins have been developed by chemically modifying the side-chain while keeping the reactive beta-lactam ring intact. This changes the shape of the molecule, making it harder to fit into the active site of the penicillinase enzyme. Modifying the side-chain can also be used to increase the bioavailability of the drug by adding more polar groups. An example would be the commonly sold form of penicillin, known as **amoxicillin**.

benzyl penicillin · amoxicillin

Despite the success of modifying the side-chain, some strains of bacteria (often called 'superbugs') have now become resistant to all the common modifications of penicillin, as well as to other antibiotics. This has partly resulted from **overprescription** of penicillin, allowing the bacteria increased exposure to the antibiotic, so increasing the chances of a resistant strain arising by a random mutation in the genetic code of the bacteria.

It is very important that patients finish the course of antibiotics, even after the symptoms of the disease have decreased. This decreases the chances that any bacteria survive long enough to develop resistance to the antibiotic. Antibiotics must also be disposed of correctly to prevent them entering the environment where their exposure to microorganisms can give further opportunity for resistance to arise (see Chapter 6).

ASPIRIN AND PENICILLIN

1. Outline how a mild analgesic, such as aspirin, relieves pain. [2]

....

....

....

2. (a) Outline the main steps in the laboratory synthesis of a pure sample of aspirin from salicylic acid. [4]

....

....

....

....

    (b) Explain two methods that can be used to evaluate the purity of a sample of aspirin. [4]

....

....

....

....

3. Explain the meaning of the term 'synergistic effect', using aspirin with alcohol as an example. [2]

....

....

4. (a) Ibuprofen, like aspirin is commonly sold as its sodium salt. Write a balanced equation to show the formation of sodium ibuprofen from ibuprofen by reaction with a suitable reagent. [2]

....

....

    (b) Explain how this reaction can be used to increase the bioavailability of drugs such as ibuprofen. [2]

....

....

5. Identify one functional group that occurs in both aspirin and the general structure of penicillins, and one functional group that occurs only in aspirin. [2]

....

....

....

6. Explain the action of penicillins, including the importance of the beta-lactam ring.[3]

....

....

....

....

7. Explain why overprescription of antibiotics, such as penicillin, has become a problem, and explain how modification of the side chain can help to overcome the problem.[4]

....

....

....

....

....

Chapter 3: Opiates

Opiates, such as **morphine** and **codeine**, are natural narcotic analgesics that are derived from the opium poppy. These are **strong analgesics**, which work by temporarily bonding to **opioid receptor** sites in the brain, supressing the transmission of pain impulses. They work because their structure resembles that of natural painkillers called endorphins. This is in contrast to the mode of action of mild analgesics, such as aspirin, which act at the site of the pain (see Chapter 2).

Figure 3.1: **Opium poppy**

Strong analgesics are used in medical situations when high levels of pain relief are needed and addiction (see section 3.1) is not likely to be a problem. Examples of the use of morphine include:

- short-term pain relief after major injury or surgery;
- palliative care (making the patient comfortable) near to the end of life.

Codeine is much less effective, but has a higher therapeutic window. It can be sold without prescription and low doses are often combined with mild analgesics, such as paracetamol or ibuprofen. It also has **antitussive** (cough supressing) properties, so is sometimes included in cough syrups.

Take care to use the correct terms for the names of functional groups: for example, 'hydroxide' would not be accepted for 'hydroxyl'. Also, don't confuse 'ether' with 'ester'.

The structures of morphine and codeine are very similar. Codeine has an ether group in place of one of the hydroxyl groups on the benzene ring. This can be synthesised from morphine by a **nucleophilic substitution** reaction with a suitable methylating reagent. The structures of morphine, codeine and diamorphine are given the *Chemistry Data Booklet*.

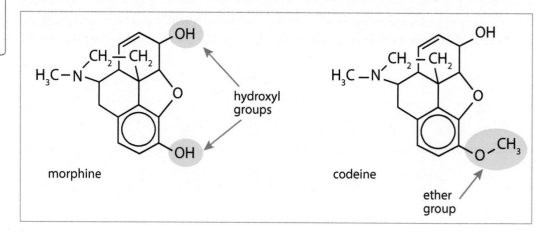

Diamorphine (heroin) is synthesised from morphine by an esterification reaction using ethanoic acid or a more reactive derivative, such as ethanoic anhydride (see the synthesis of aspirin in Chapter 2). This condensation reaction converts the two hydroxyl groups on morphine into two ester groups.

Diamorphine is much more potent than morphine because the ester groups are less polar than the hydroxyl groups. This improves its bioavailability as the less polar molecule is more soluble in lipids. This allows it to cross the blood-brain barrier and reach the opioid receptor sites more quickly. The lipid-based barrier that surrounds the tissue in the brain and central nervous system is designed to protect the brain against potentially neurotoxic water-soluble compounds in the blood.

diamorphine

ester groups

3.1 Addiction and side effects

When opiate molecules bind to the opioid receptors in the brain, the patient will experience feelings of relaxation and euphoria, as well as a reduction in pain. This leads to psychological addiction, as the patient feels very 'low' once the effects of the drug have worn off. Therefore, they want to take the drug again. Continued use of the drug can lead to tolerance, with higher doses needed to have the same original effect. This leads to increased problems due to side effects. Side effects of opiates include:

- Constipation
- Nausea and vomiting
- Sedation
- Reduction in breathing rate
- Depression and apathy
- Dizziness
- Kidney failure with long-term use.

Long-term users of opiates also become dependent on the drug, as the body adapts to its continual presence. This results in unpleasant withdrawal symptoms if the drug is not taken, such as chills, sweats, diarrhoea, anxiety, muscle cramps, and insomnia.

3.2 Advantages and disadvantages of opiates

Some of the advantages and disadvantages of using strong analgesics rather than mild analgesics for pain relief are summarised below.

Advantages	Disadvantages
Much stronger pain relief	Addiction, leading to dependence and withdrawal symptoms
Rapid action when administered intravenously	Side effects, including constipation, nausea and kidney failure (see above)
Wide therapeutic window	Tolerance, leading to increased side effects and risk of overdose
Induces relaxation/relief of anxiety	Lack of self-control/depression and apathy
Antitussive (codeine)	Social problems due to drug abuse, such as crime, poor living conditions etc.

1. Outline how a strong analgesic, such as codeine, relieves pain. [3]

....

....

....

....

2. The structure shown is a simplified version of a molecule of morphine.

OH

OH

(a) Use this structure to write a balanced equation to illustrate the synthesis of diamorphine from morphine, using a suitable reagent. [2]

....

....

(b) Explain why diamorphine is much more potent than morphine. [4]

....

....

....

....

....

3. Describe and explain *two* disadvantages of using strong analgesics, such as morphine, for pain relief. [4]

....

....

....

....

....

Chapter 4:   pH Regulation of the Stomach

4.1   Excess stomach acid

The digestive fluid secreted into the stomach from the lining of the stomach normally contains hydrochloric acid with a concentration of between 0.05 and 0.10 mol dm-3. The acid is used to kill harmful bacteria, as well as providing the optimum pH for the enzymes that catalyse the hydrolysis of protein. However, an excess of stomach acid can result in the following problems:

- **Acid reflux** (heartburn): a burning sensation when acid flows up into the oesophagus
- **Peptic ulcers**: a painful open sore in the lining of the stomach or small intestine.

Causes of excess stomach acid include bacterial infection or the continual use of anti-inflammatory drugs, such as aspirin. It can also be made worse by excess amounts of fatty foods, alcohol, and carbonated drinks in the diet. Excess stomach acid can therefore be reduced to some extent by controlling the diet, but if further treatment is needed, there are two approaches: (1) antacids and (2) drugs which inhibit the production acid.

4.2   Antacids

These contain a base that can neutralise the excess acid. Examples bases in common antacids include:

- Calcium hydroxide
- Magnesium hydroxide
- Aluminium hydroxide
- Sodium carbonate
- Sodium bicarbonate (sodium hydrogen carbonate).

The base rapidly neutralises the acid in a non-specific reaction to give a salt, water and (in the case of carbonates) carbon dioxide gas.

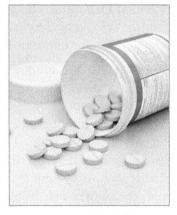

Figure 4.1: **Antacid tablets**

▶   acid + metal hydroxide → salt + water

For example:

hydrochloric acid + magnesium hydroxide → magnesium chloride + water

$$2HCl\,(aq)\ +\ Mg(OH)_2\,(s)\ \rightarrow\ MgCl_2\,(aq)\ +\ 2H_2O\,(l)$$

Make sure that you know (i) the general forms of these neutralisation reactions, and (ii) how to deduce the formulae of all the relevant compounds. Then you can construct and balance an equation for any given antacid.

▶   acid + metal (hydrogen) carbonate → salt + water + carbon dioxide

For example:

hydrochloric acid + sodium bicarbonate → sodium chloride + water + carbon dioxide

$$HCl\,(aq) + NaHCO_3\,(aq) \rightarrow NaCl\,(aq) + H_2O\,(l) + CO_2\,(g)$$

These equations can be used to calculate the amounts of antacid needed, as in the example below.

If the concentration of hydrochloric acid in a patient's stomach is $0.115\,mol\,dm^{-3}$, and the stomach has a volume of fluid of $1.00\,dm^3$, calculate the number of 200 mg tablets of aluminium hydroxide needed to reduce the concentration to a safe level, i.e. to below $0.100\,mol\,dm^{-3}$.

Minimum amount of HCl needed to react $= 0.115\,mol - 0.100\,mol = 0.015\,mol$

Balanced equation: $3\,HCl + Al(OH)_3 \rightarrow AlCl_3 + 3\,H_2O$, so ratio $= 3:1$

Amount of $Al(OH)_3$ needed $= 0.015 \div 3 = 0.005\,mol$

Mass of $Al(OH)_3$ needed: $m = n \times M_r, = 0.005\,mol \times 78.01\,gmol^{-1} = 0.390\,g = 2$ tablets

4.3   Drugs which inhibit the production of acid

The other approach to treating excess stomach acid is to inhibit the secretion of the acid by the cells in the lining of the stomach. These drugs are not as quick acting as antacids, but they have a much longer-term effect. This makes them much more suitable for treatment of peptic ulcers and generally preventing the damage due to continual over-production of acid. There are two types of drug which have been used for this in recent years.

4.3.1   H₂ agonists

Note that the term 'H₂' is not referring to hydrogen gas here, but to distinguish these receptors from another type of histamine receptor, 'H₁', that is involved in the inflammation responses normally treated by antihistamines.

Drugs such as **ranitidine** (Zantac) block the action of **histamine**. The secretion of acid from the cells lining the stomach is normally stimulated by the hormone histamine.

The structure of ranitidine is given in the *Chemistry Data Booklet*. The ranitidine molecule prevents the secretion of this acid by reversibly binding to the H₂ histamine receptors in the cells. This is possible because part of the ranitidine molecule is a similar shape to histamine and so fits into the receptor side. This competes with histamine and prevents it from binding.

ranitidine

Note the region with similar shape to histamine

histamine

4.3.2   Proton pump inhibitors

H₂ agonists have more recently been replaced by proton pump inhibitors, such as **omeprazole** (Prilosec) and **esomeprazole** (Nexium). These block the enzyme responsible for the pumping the H⁺ ions out of the cells and into the stomach. They are much more effective than H₂ agonists because their action is irreversible, so they permanently deactivate the proton pump.

The structure of omeprazole is given in the *Chemistry Data Booklet*. Esomeprazole has an identical structure except that the 3D orientation of the groups around the S atom is different.

omeprazole

For HL students, the two molecules are optical isomers, due to the presence of a chiral centre.

active form of omeprazole

Note the rearrangement of the atoms here

In the form shown above, the drug is not active but is less polar than the active form. This means that it will more easily cross the lipid based cell membrane into the cells. Once the molecule is inside the cell, it becomes charged and part of it rearranges as a result of metabolic reactions inside the cell. This creates the **active form** that binds to the proton pump. It is not uncommon with drugs that the active form of the drug is only created after it has been processed in some way by metabolic processes in the body.

This is similar to the way that diamorphine crosses the blood-brain barrier: see Chapter 3.)

4.4   Buffer solutions

Many drugs will only be active within a certain range of pH. Also some drugs are themselves acidic or basic and so would alter the pH of the fluids in the body, causing damage to the body. In order to keep pH relatively constant when a drug is administered, a **buffer solution** is added to the drug formulation.

A buffer solution is one that *resists changes in pH* when small amounts of acid or alkali are added. A buffer solution is composed of a mixture of a weak acid and its conjugate base, or a mixture of a weak base and its conjugate acid. Either way, as long as both species are present in reasonable amounts, the equilibrium between the protonated and deprotonated species will be able to respond to the addition of H^+ ions or OH^- ions. This happens as the equilibrium position shifts to oppose the change, removing the added ions, and so minimising the effect of the added acid or alkali.

For HA, a typical weak acid:

Any added H^+ ions are removed as the equilibrium can shift **left** in response, i.e. $H^+ + A^- \rightarrow HA$

$$HA \rightleftharpoons H^+ + A^-$$

Any added OH^- ions are removed as they combine with H^+ ions to give water:
    $H^+ + OH^- \rightarrow H_2O$
The resulting decrease in $[H^+]$ causes the equilibrium to shift
right in response, i.e. $HA \rightarrow H^+ + A^-$
Overall this gives: $HA + OH^- \rightarrow H_2O + A^-$

The pH of a buffer solution can be calculated as long as the pK_a of the weak acid is known, as well as the relative concentrations of the acid and its conjugate base in the mixture. The *Chemistry Data Booklet* gives pK_a values for a range of organic acids in section 21.

The calculation of the pH of a buffer solution follows directly on from HL topic 18. However, SL students might still be asked to use this expression by just plugging in the numbers.

The necessary mathematical expression, known as the Henderson-Hasselbalch equation, is given in section 1 of the *Chemistry Data Booklet*:

$$pH = pK_a + \log\left(\frac{[A^-]}{[HA]}\right)$$

A buffer solution is made by dissolving 3.94 g of sodium propanoate (C_2H_5COONa) into 100 cm³ of a 0.200 mol dm⁻³ solution of propanoic acid. Use the pK_a value for propanoic acid from the *Chemistry Data Booklet* to calculate the pH of the buffer solution.

Amount of sodium propanoate, $n = m/M_r = 3.94\,g \div 96.07\,g\,mol^{-1} = 0.0400\,mol$

Concentration of sodium propanoate, $c = n/v = 0.0400\,mol \div 0.100\,dm^3 = 0.400\,mol\,dm^{-3}$

pK_a for propanoic acid (from the *Chemistry Data Booklet*) = 4.97

pH of the buffer solution $= pK_a + \log([A^-]/[HA]) = 4.97 + \log(0.400/0.200)$
                                              $= 4.97 + \log 2 = 4.97 + 0.301 = \textbf{5.17}$

It is quite common for buffer solutions to be made by partially neutralising an excess of the weak acid with a strong base. This creates the conjugate base of the acid as a product of the reaction. The amount of weak acid remaining in the mixture must be calculated by subtracting the amount of acid that has reacted from the amount originally present.

Note that in this example the ratio of moles, rather than concentration of A⁻ and HA, could have been used directly in the Henderson-Hasselbalch equation. This is because the volume is the same for both substances in the final mixture.

A buffer solution is made by adding 400 cm³ of 0.0500 mol dm⁻³ sodium hydroxide to 100 cm³ of a 0.500 mol dm⁻³ solution of methanoic acid. Calculate final amounts of methanoic acid and sodium methanoate in moles and then use the pK_a value for methanoic acid from section 21 of the *Chemistry Data Booklet* to calculate the pH of the buffer solution.

Initial amount of HCOOH, $n = c \times v = 0.100\,dm^3 \times 0.500\,mol\,dm^{-3} = 0.0500\,mol$

Added amount of NaOH, $n = c \times v = 0.400\,dm^3 \times 0.0500\,mol\,dm^{-3} = 0.0200\,mol$

Reaction:	HCOOH	+	NaOH	→	HCOONa	+	H₂O
Initial amounts:	0.0500 mol		0.0200 mol		0 mol		
Final amounts:	0.0300 mol		0 mol		0.0200 mol		

Total volume = 400 cm³ + 100 cm³ = 0.500 dm³, so divide moles by this volume, to give final concentrations:

                 0.0600 mol dm⁻³   and   0.0400 mol dm⁻³

pK_a for methanoic acid (from *Chemistry Data Booklet*) = 3.75

pH of the buffer solution $= pK_a + \log([A^-]/[HA]) = 3.75 + \log(0.0400/0.0600)$
                                              $= 3.75 + \log 0.667 = 3.75 + -0.176 = \textbf{3.57}$

1. The following experiment was carried out to determine the % purity of calcium carbonate in a commercial brand of antacid. Write a balanced equation for the reaction of the tablets with the acid, and calculate the % by mass of calcium carbonate in the tablets, stating one assumption made.

    Two 200 mg antacid tablets were crushed and dissolved in 100.0 ± 0.1 cm³ of 0.100 mol dm³ hydrochloric acid (an excess). When the reaction had finished, the remaining mixture was titrated with 0.200 mol dm³ sodium hydroxide solution. It was found that an average 25.2 ± 0.1 cm³ of alkali was needed to neutralise the excess acid in the mixture. [5]

....

....

....

....

....

....

2. Outline the difference between the way that an antacid and ranitidine (Zantac) control the pH of the stomach, and give one advantage of each method. [4]

....

....

....

....

....

3. Explain the term 'active metabolite' as applied to drugs, using omeprazole as an example. [2]

....

....

4. A buffer solution made from a mixture of benzoic acid and sodium benzoate needs to have a pH of 4.0. Use the pK_a value for benzoic acid given in the *Chemistry Data Booklet* to calculate the ratio of benzoic acid to sodium benzoate required to obtain this pH. [3]

....

....

....

....

Chapter 5: Antiviral Medications

Viruses and **bacteria** are both responsible for a wide range of diseases. Many bacteria, however, coexist with the human body and do not cause harm, and some (such as bacteria in the gut) are beneficial to the normal working of the healthy body. Bacteria are single-celled organisms, and those which cause disease do so by either damaging tissues as they feed or by producing toxic compounds as waste products. Bacterial infections can be treated by antibiotics such as penicillins, which kill the bacterial cells (see Chapter 2).

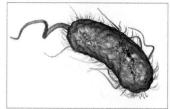

Figure 5.1: **Illustrations of a virus (top) and bacterium (not to equivalent scale)**

Viruses differ from bacteria in a number of ways:

- viruses are generally much smaller than bacteria;
- viruses are not living cells, but are made from DNA or RNA surrounded by a protein coat;
- viruses do not have a cell wall, nucleus or cytoplasm;
- viruses cannot reproduce without invading a host cell;
- viruses are always parasitic.

Viruses are more difficult to target with drugs than bacteria because they lack a cell structure and only reproduce inside living cells. Many viruses also mutate easily and frequently. This leads to changes in the composition of their protein coat or other key proteins that can lead to resistance to drugs.

Antiviral drugs may work by:

- altering the cell's genetic material so that the virus cannot use it to multiply;
- preventing the viruses from multiplying by blocking enzyme activity involved with either replication of DNA/RNA within the host cell, or the release of the new viruses.

Examples of antiviral drugs include **oseltamivir** (Tamiflu) and **zanamivir** (Relenza). These work as preventative agents against flu viruses. They both work by inhibiting the enzyme **neuraminidase**, which is produced by the virus as part of the mechanism that allows the new viruses to leave the host cell after replication.

The structures of oseltamivir and zanamivir are given in the *Chemistry Data Booklet*.

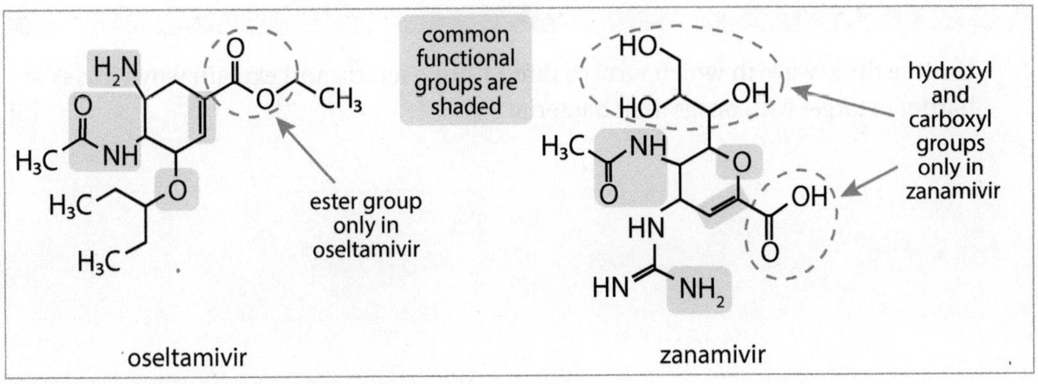

Figure 5.2: **Structures of oseltamivir and zanamivir**

They have a number of functional groups in common, but some are unique to either oseltamivir or zanamivir, as shown in Figure 5.2.

AIDS, which is caused by the **HIV virus**, has been a particularly difficult disease to treat for several reasons.

- The virus attacks the 'T-cells' that are essential to the functioning of the immune system, so it prevents the normal immune response involved in recovering from a viral infection.
- The virus coats itself in proteins from the host cell, so it makes it very hard to distinguish from human cells.
- The virus has a very high turnover and regularly mutates, which leads to resistance
- The virus can lie dormant inside the host cells for many years, which prevents its total eradication.

A large amount of research has been needed to produce anti-retroviral drugs that can overcome these difficulties. This has meant that they are very expensive, making them too expensive for poorer communities in developing countries where the disease is prevalent.

The control of the drug has also been hindered by sociocultural issues, for example:

- the stigma attached to diagnosis in some cultures may delay or inhibit treatment;
- cultural resistance to cheaper preventative measures, such as use of condoms;
- difficulties controlling illegal activities such as prostitution.

The impact of this has been devastating in some communities, where many parents have died of the disease, leaving many orphans.

1. Outline three ways in which viruses differ from bacteria and explain why viruses are harder to target with drugs than bacteria. [5]

....

....

....

....

....

....

2. Explain how zanamivir (Relenza) works as a preventative agent against the flu virus. [3]

....

....

....

....

3. Use the structures given in section 37 of the *Chemistry Data Booklet* to name three functional groups that are found in both oseltamivir and zanamivir. [3]

....

....

....

....

4. Resistance has made the AIDS virus hard to treat. Explain how resistance to a drug arises and suggest *two ways* to combat the problem of drug resistance. [4]

....

....

....

....

....

Chapter 6: Environmental Impact of Some Medications

6.1 Disposal of waste

The development of drugs must consider not only the effects on the patients, but also the impact that the drug or waste products from its production and use might have on other people or the environment. These ethical considerations are an important aspect of medicinal chemistry.

6.1.1 Nuclear waste

Nuclear waste is potentially a significant problem for medical health workers, the general public, and the environment, due to the damage that ionising radiation can do to living tissue. Exposure to nuclear waste can lead to reproductive problems and cancers. Nuclear waste can be classified by considering:

Figure 6.1: **A type of high-level waste container**

1. the amount of ionising radiation given off, and
2. how long it will take before the waste decays to a safe level.

High-level waste (HLW) is waste that gives off large amounts of ionising radiation for a long time. This requires significant amounts of shielding and cooling and can only be disposed of by reprocessing and then, after it has decayed to a safer level, encasing in steel and concrete and burying deep underground. This type of high-level waste is typically produced by nuclear reactors or nuclear processing plants. However, some of the isotopes used in radiotherapy will give off sufficient amounts of ionising radiation to require shielding—but not cooling. This is sometimes categorised separately as **Intermediate-level waste (ILW)**. This is treated the same as HLW but the amount of shielding required is less, and burial does not have to be so deep.

Figure 6.2: **Low-level waste from medical procedures**

Low-level waste (LLW) is waste that gives off small amounts of ionising radiation for a short time and includes the majority of medical waste. This would include radioactive isotopes used as tracers and some radiotherapy treatments.

It would also include equipment that has been in contact with radioactive materials, such as syringes, disposable gloves, and other protective equipment. Once most of the isotope has decayed, the ionising radiation from this category of waste will be too low to be harmful once dispersed in the environment and, therefore, it can be disposed by landfill or by incineration.

6.1.2 Antibiotic waste

Antibiotic resistance occurs when microorganisms become resistant to antibacterials (see Chapter 2). The greater the exposure that the microorganisms get to the antibiotic, the greater the chance that a mutation will arise that can lead to resistance. Therefore, there is a danger from improper disposal of waste containing antibiotics. If it is just dumped or washed away into the environment it can come into contact with a wide variety of microorganisms. Antibiotic waste can be produced by many sources, including the following examples:

- the disposal of antibiotic ingredients from factories making the antibiotics;
- the disposal of out-of-date antibiotic medications by hospitals and pharmacies;
- antibiotics that are used widely as a prophylactic in farming to protect animals against diseases. The antibiotic is typically added to the animal feed, but this makes it very easy for some to get into the environment.

To combat the problem, medical antibiotics need to be destroyed (for example, by incineration) or immobilised before disposal (for example, by encasing in concrete). To reduce the use of antibiotics in farming, it may require changes to intensive farming practices to improve animal hygiene.

6.1.3 Solvents

Many drugs are produced by reactions that require solvents other than water. These include halogenoalkanes that are known to contribute to depletion of the ozone layer. Many of these chlorinated solvents are also non-biodegradable, so they can accumulate in the environment. These and other solvents are also toxic to humans and/or animals. Therefore, it is important that solvents are not just allowed to evaporate. To combat the problem the solvents should ideally be replaced by alternative non-toxic solvents, such as **supercritical** CO_2. If that is not possible, the solvent should be recovered by distillation and recycled.

6.2   Green chemistry

Green chemistry, also called sustainable chemistry, is an approach to chemical research and engineering that seeks to minimise the production and release to the environment of hazardous substances. This involves consideration of the following criteria.

- Are processes used that *maximise the amount of raw material* that ends up in the product? This can be done by a combination of

  (a)   using processes that involve fewer steps, as some material is always lost at each step due to the inevitable loss of **percentage yield** during the process, and

  (b)   using processes with higher **atom economy**: a measure of the % by mass of reactant(s) that ends up in the product according to the balanced equation.

- Does the process *avoid the production of waste* materials?
- Are *renewable materials used* as raw materials and energy sources?
- Are non-toxic, *environmentally safe substances used* throughout?
- Are the processes *energy efficient*?

Atom economy is referred to briefly in core topic 1.1. It is relatively easy to work out, so it might be worth practising just in case it appears in a question.

An example is the production of the mild analgesic, **ibuprofen** from the raw material, 2-methylpropylbenzene.

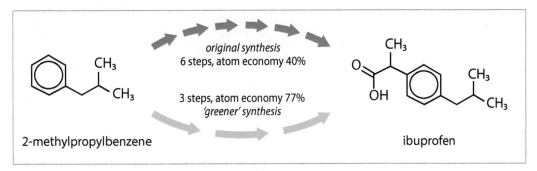

Figure 6.3: **Improving sustainability of ibuprofen manufacture**

The original method involved six steps. However, this was replaced by a process involving only three steps, so there is a higher overall percentage yield, as well as a higher atom economy of 77%.

Another example is the synthesis of **shikimic acid**, which is a precursor for the antiviral drug **Tamiflu** (oseltamivir), used in treatment of influenza (see Chapter 5). This was originally synthesised from a plant extract in ten steps, each with the production of waste material and a very low overall percentage yield of 2–7%. It is now synthesised in one step by genetically modified *E. coli* bacteria, at lower temperatures and avoiding the use of toxic solvents.

shikimic acid

ENVIRONMENTAL IMPACT OF SOME MEDICATIONS

1. State *two* examples of radioactive medical waste with different levels of radioactivity, and outline how each can be disposed of with minimal impact on the environment.
[4]

....

....

....

....

....

....

2. State *two* environmental issues related to solvents left-over from drug production. [2]

....

....

....

3. Outline how green chemistry was used to reduce the environmental impact of the production of the precursor for Tamiflu.
[3]

....

....

....

....

....

Chapter 7: Taxol: A Chiral Auxiliary Case Study (HL only)

Taxol (also known as **Paclitaxel**) is a drug that is commonly used to treat several different forms of cancer. It does this by binding to a protein called **β-tubulin** that is essential for cell division. This prevents the cancer cells multiplying.

For this topic, it would be helpful to revise optical isomerism, which is covered in HL topic 20.3.

7.1   Obtaining the drug

The compound occurs naturally in the bark of the **Pacific Yew tree.** However, this tree is scarce and slow growing. Therefore, extracting the drug from this resource is expensive. There are also environmental concerns that too many trees will be killed for their bark, leading to extinction of the species in the wild.

To provide an alternative source of the drug, it has been synthetically produced from simpler molecules, but the total synthesis of such a large molecule involves many steps, resulting in a very low yield. Also, the molecule contains 11 chiral centres in total (as shown in Figure 7.1).

This means that there are theoretically $2^{11} = 2,048$ different stereoisomers of the compound. Only one of these stereoisomers is active, as each of the 11 chiral centres must be in the correct enantiomeric form to give the whole molecule the correct 3D shape to fit into the particular protein, illustrated in Figure 7.2.

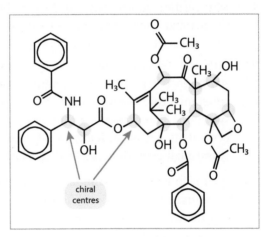

Figure 7.1: **The structure of Taxol, showing chiral centres**

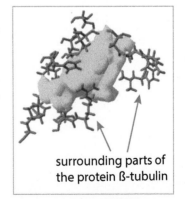

Figure 7.2: **The 3D shape of the Taxol binding site**

The synthesis of one particular stereoisomer of an optically active molecule can be very difficult, as organic reactions often produce both enantiomers when a chiral centre is formed. For example, electrophilic addition of hydrogen chloride to but-1-ene (which is not chiral), will produce a racemic mixture of both enantiomers of 2-chlorobutane in equal proportions.

In contrast, many metabolic reactions in living organisms can produce just one stereoisomer, as the enzymes catalysing the reaction are asymmetric, so that only one particular 3D shape can bind into the active site of the enzyme and form the product.

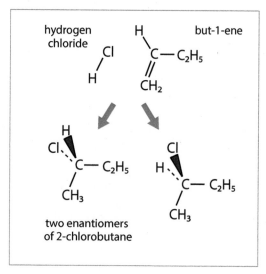

Figure 7.3: **Two enantiomers of 2-chlorobutane**

7.2 Synthesis of Taxol

The chiral synthesis of Taxol without further damage to the Pacific yew population has been achieved by the following strategy.

1. Starting the synthesis with **10-deacetylbaccatin III**, a compound that occurs naturally in the much more common **European Yew tree**, and already contains nine out of the 11 chiral centres in their correct enantiomeric form.

2. The use of a **chiral auxiliary** to ensure that the two remaining chiral centres are synthesised in their correct enantiomeric form. A chiral auxiliary is an optically active substance that is temporarily added to the reactant molecule during an organic synthesis. The presence of the chiral auxiliary causes the subsequent steps to be carried out asymmetrically with the selective formation of a single enantiomer. The chiral auxiliary is then removed at a later stage.

The scheme in Figure 7.4 summarises the synthesis of Taxol using a chiral auxiliary. Note that this scheme has been simplified from the full synthetic route and does not show all the reagents, intermediate steps, and changes in functional groups.

The synthesis of Taxol is very complex, and you are not expected to know all the details. It is the role of the chiral auxiliary that is most important to understand.

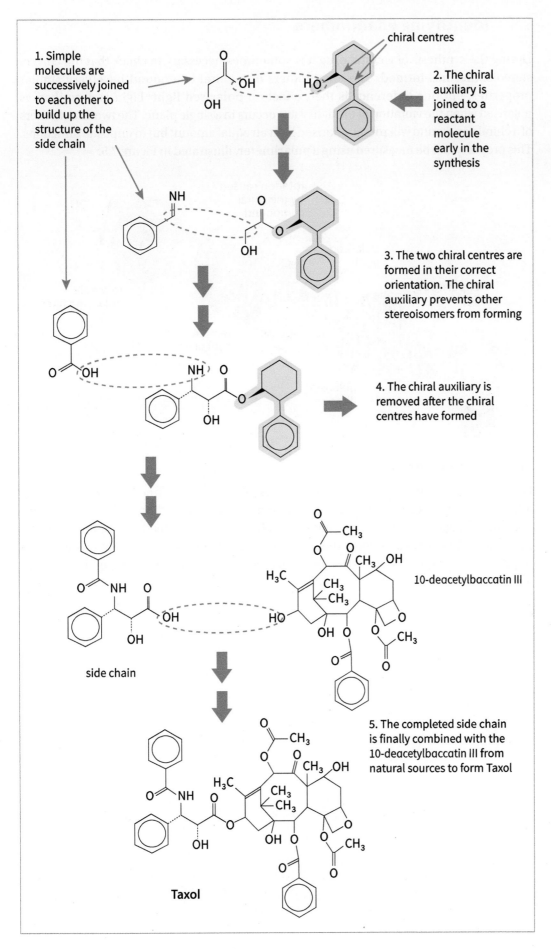

Figure 7.4: **Synthesis of Taxol using a chiral auxiliary**

7.3   Identifying enantiomers

During the synthesis of a chiral drug it is sometimes necessary to check that the correct stereoisomer has formed. The enantiomers of a chiral compound have very similar properties, but one difference is their effect on **polarised light**. Light is described as polarised when the vibration of the light wave occurs in a single plane. The two enantiomers of a chiral compound will rotate polarised light an equal amount but in opposite directions. This property can be measured using a **polarimeter**, illustrated in Figure 7.5.

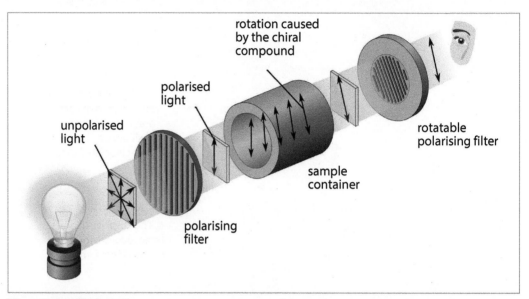

Figure 7.5: **Polarimeter**

Light from most natural sources contains waves vibrating in all directions, so a polarising filter is needed to select only light in one plane. The sample is then placed in the beam of polarised light. The degree of rotation can be detected by steadily rotating a second polarising filter placed beyond the sample until the light seen coming through it is brightest. The angle of rotation can be measured using a scale on the second polarising filter.

1. State a natural source for the anti-cancer drug Taxol, and explain why it is now more commonly produced using chemical synthesis. [3]

....

....

....

....

2. Describe how a chiral auxiliary is used in drug synthesis. [3]

....

....

....

....

3. [5]

(a) Explain how a polarimeter can be used to distinguish between two samples, each containing a different enantiomer of a chiral compound.

....

....

....

....

(b) Describe and explain the observed effect when a racemic mixture is put into a polarimeter.

....

....

....

....

....

....

Chapter 8:   Nuclear Medicine (HL only)

Nuclear medicine uses radioisotopes to either diagnose or treat diseases, especially cancer. Radioisotopes have unstable nuclei that emit ionising radiation in the form of a number of types of particle or ray. Nuclear reactions involving **alpha particles**, **beta particles**, **gamma rays**, **protons**, **neutrons** and **positrons** are all used for medical treatment.

8.1   Nuclear equations

Nuclear equations can be written to summarise the changes in nuclear particles before and after a nuclear reaction. Some of these particles have more than one accepted way of representing them: for example, an alpha particle, $^4_2\alpha$, is the same as the nucleus of a helium atom, $^4_2$He, so either symbol can be used. Note that unlike in normal chemical equations, any (+/–) charge is not always shown; as a nuclear equation does not include the orbiting electrons that balance the overall positive charge of the nucleus. The table below shows alternative symbols for the commonly-emitted particles.

Particle/ray	alpha	beta	gamma	proton	neutron	positron
Symbol(s)	$^4_2$He or $^4_2\alpha$	$^0_{-1}e$ or $^0_{-1}\beta$	$^0_0\gamma$ or just γ	$^1_1$H or ^1_1p	$^1_0 n$	$^0_1 e$ or $^0_1\beta$

Although beta particles are electrons, in nuclear reactions they are ***produced from the nucleus*** and are independent of any orbiting electrons. Positrons are the anti-particle of the electron and do not normally exist in stable atoms.

e.g.

bismuth-213	$\rightarrow$	thallium-209	+	α particle
$^{213}_{83}$Bi	$\rightarrow$	$^{209}_{81}$Tl	+	$^4_2$He

↑
Emission of an α particle always decreases the mass number by 4 and the atomic number by 2

You could be asked to balance any nuclear equation involving α or β emissions, but it is likely to be one of the common equations used in nuclear medicine, so it is worth checking that you know these.

8.1.1   Balancing nuclear equations

To balance a nuclear equation, the sum of the mass numbers and the atomic numbers of all the particles must be equal on either side of the arrow. Typically you will know the starting isotope and what type of particle is formed. Therefore, you can deduce the identity of the product isotope by balancing the total of the mass and atomic number as shown in the following worked examples.

Yttrium-90 is used widely in radiotherapy and decays by emitting a β particle. Write a nuclear decay equation for this process.

1. Write the known particles:

    $$^{90}_{39}Y \rightarrow ^{A}_{Z}X + ^{0}_{-1}\beta$$

2. Deduce the mass and atomic numbers (A and Z) of the product isotope (X) needed to make the total of the mass and atomic numbers either side of the arrow equal:

    $$^{90}_{39}Y \rightarrow ^{90}_{40}X + ^{0}_{-1}\beta$$

    Emission of β particle just increases the atomic number by 1

3. Identify the product isotope from its atomic number using the Periodic table.

    $$^{90}_{39}Y \rightarrow ^{90}_{40}Zr + ^{0}_{-1}\beta$$

8.2 Medical imaging

There are a number of techniques that can be used to produce an image of organs inside the body. These include:

- Computed tomography (CT) using X-rays
- Ultrasound
- Nuclear magnetic resonance imaging (MRI)
- Positron emission tomography (PET)
- Imaging using a radioactive tracer such as technetium-99m.

Of these, CT, ultrasound and MRI would not be classed as nuclear medicine, as they do not involve the use of radioisotopes.

Magnetic resonance imaging (MRI) uses the same ^{1}H NMR technology that is used in organic chemistry to identify the chemical environment of protons (see core topic 11.3). To produce an image of body tissues, the NMR spectrometer is set to detect the radio frequency radiation emitted as the O–H bonded protons in water molecules realign in the magnetic field. The human body contains water throughout, but the chemical environment of the protons in the water is altered slightly by the type of cell or tissue containing the water. The different chemical environments cause the protons to realign at slightly different rates, which can be detected and shown as different shading on the image.

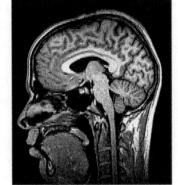

Figure 8.1: **MRI scan of the head**

Positron emission tomography (PET) uses a radioisotope that is a positron (β$^+$) emitter. When a positron is emitted from the nucleus, it is immediately annihilated by colliding with the nearest orbiting electron, causing the production of two high energy gamma rays.

positron	+	electron	→	two gamma rays
$^{0}_{1}e$	+	$^{0}_{-1}e$	→	$2^{0}_{0}\gamma$

The most common example of PET uses the isotope fluorine-18, which decays to give oxygen-18.

fluorine-18	→	oxygen-18	+	positron
$^{18}_{9}F$	→	$^{18}_{8}O$	+	$^{0}_{1}e$

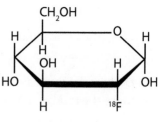

The fluorine isotope attached to glucose by replacing the OH group on the second carbon of the glucose. The parts of the body that are actively metabolising glucose, such as the brain or cancer cells, will take up the 2-[18]fluorodeoxyglucose more rapidly than other cells. A gamma ray detector in the scanner is then used to show up on an image where the production of gamma rays is more concentrated.

2-[18] fluorodeoxyglucose

Radioactive tracer imaging uses a radioisotope to track the distribution of a particular substance in the body. This is done by attaching the radioisotope to the compound of interest and then using a scanner to detect the location of the radiation emitted. The most common radioisotope used for this is **technetium-99m**. This is an unstable form of isotope technetium-99, which will decay to the stable form with the emission of a gamma ray.

technetium-99m	→	technetium-99	+	gamma ray
$^{99m}_{43}Tc$	→	$^{99}_{43}Tc$	+	$^{0}_{0}\gamma$

It is particularly suitable for imaging for the following reasons.

- It is a gamma ray emitter:
  - gamma rays are most easily detected, so only small quantities of the isotope can be used;
  - most of the energy of the rays leaves the body and does not cause significant local damage to tissues.

- It has a half-life of only 6 hours, so it will remain in the body long enough to allow detection, but then the activity will have fallen to almost zero within a few days, so lessening the chance of longer term radiation damage.

- The isotope it decays to has a low level of radioactivity, so also lessens the chance of longer term radiation damage.

- As a transition metal, it readily forms complex ions with a range of ligands, which allows it to be readily attached to a variety of other molecules for transport to the site of interest in the body.

- It is relatively easy to produce from uranium produced by nuclear reactors.

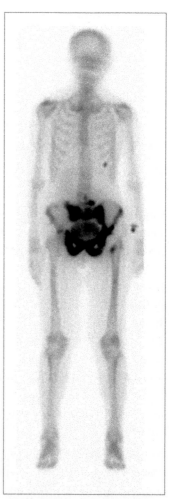

Figure 8.2: Tc-99m bone scan showing cancer in the bone

8.3 Radiotherapy

Radiotherapy is commonly used in cancer treatment to kill the cancer cells by exposing them to the high energy radiation. It can be administered in two ways.

1. **Externally** by passing X-rays or gamma rays through the body aimed at the cancer cells.

2. **Internally** by placing a radioisotope inside the body.

Three common isotopes used for internal radiotherapy include **lutetium-177, yttrium-90** and **iodine-131**, which are all beta emitters that decay in one step to produce a stable, non-toxic product.

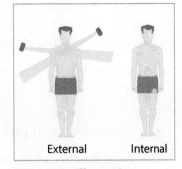

Figure 8.3: **Illustration of external vs. internal radiotherapy**

$$\text{lutetium-177} \rightarrow \text{hafnium-177} + \beta \text{ particle}$$
$$^{177}_{71}\text{Lu} \rightarrow ^{177}_{72}\text{Hf} + ^{0}_{-1}e$$

As beta radiation is relatively short range, the isotope needs to be administered in a way that gets as much as possible to the target tissue, while minimising the amount distributed elsewhere in the body. Yttrium-90 has proven particularly effective in the treatment of liver cancer by injection directly into the blood vessels travelling towards the liver, while lutetium-117 has been used in treatment of some intestinal and pancreatic tumours by attaching it to a hormone particularly taken up by these tissues. Iodine-131 is used to combat thyroid cancer as iodine is naturally concentrated in the body by the thyroid gland.

8.3.1 Targeted Alpha Therapy

Targeted Alpha Therapy (TAT) is a relatively new treatment that uses an alpha emitter such as bismuth-213 or lead-212, which is attached to antibodies that bind specifically to the tumour cells. It has been used effectively to combat a number of cancers, including leukaemia, melanoma, pancreatic and ovarian cancer. Heavy isotopes such as these typically decay via a number of steps, some of which are very rapid. For example, lead-212 first loses two β particles to form polonium-212, before this isotope decays to give stable lead-208 and an alpha particle.

$$\text{lead-212} \rightarrow \text{bismuth-212} \rightarrow \text{polonium-212} \rightarrow \text{lead-208} + \alpha \text{ particle}$$
$$^{212}_{82}\text{Pb} \xrightarrow{\beta} ^{212}_{83}\text{Bi} \xrightarrow{\beta} ^{212}_{84}\text{Po} \rightarrow ^{208}_{82}\text{Pb} + ^{4}_{2}\text{He}$$

This has certain advantages over the other internal radiotherapy treatments using beta emitters described above:

- the ability to target only the tumour cells makes it potentially more effective in treating secondary tumours where the cancer has spread throughout the body;

- alpha particles are more strongly ionising, and have a much shorter path length than beta emitters, so they are very effective in killing the cells immediately surrounding the isotope, but without the radiation reaching other nearby healthy tissue.

8.3.2 Boron Neutron Capture Therapy

Boron Neutron Capture Therapy (BNCT) is another new treatment that takes advantage of the strongly ionising property and short path length of alpha particles. This method also produces high energy lithium ions that contribute to killing the tumour cells. One advantage of this method is that the only isotope introduced into the body is **boron-10**, which is not radioactive, and therefore less damaging to healthy tissue. The boron-10 is incorporated into a compound that is selectively taken up by the growing tumour cells, for example, boronophenylalanine. The patient is then radiated externally with a beam of neutrons aimed at the tumour. Neutrons that collide with the boron-10 isotopes are captured and decay into high energy alpha particles and lithium ions.

$$
\begin{array}{ccccccc}
\text{boron-10} & + & \text{neutron} & \rightarrow & \text{lithium-7} & + & \alpha \text{ particle} \\
{}^{10}_{5}\text{B} & + & {}^{1}_{0}n & \rightarrow & {}^{7}_{3}\text{Li} & + & {}^{4}_{2}\text{He}
\end{array}
$$

8.3.3 Side effects of radiotherapy

There are a number of common side effects from radiotherapy that result from the damage to the DNA of healthy tissue caused by the ionising radiation. The effects are most noticeable where there is growing or regenerating tissue. Examples include:

- hair loss;
- nausea;
- fatigue;
- sterility.

8.4 Calculating the amount of radioactive material decayed after a certain period of time

See HL topic 16.1 for a reminder of the graphs produced by a first order chemical reaction.

Radioactive decay is a first order process as the rate of decay is proportional to the amount of isotope remaining. Different isotopes have very different probabilities of decaying, but the decay curve for any isotope will always be a first order exponential curve, as seen for a the graph of concentration of reactant vs. time for a first order chemical reaction. The rate that different radioisotopes decay can be compared by considering their **half-life**: the time taken for the amount of isotope to fall by half. This will be constant for a first order process whatever the starting amount happens to be. The half-life for any given isotope can be found in a suitable data book (although they are not given in the *Chemistry Data Booklet*, so half-lives would be given in any question that required a calculation).

Note that it will take a little over 3 half-lives to fall to 10% of the original activity and a little over 6 half-lives to fall to just over 1%.

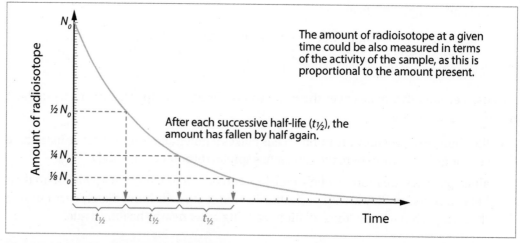

Figure 8.4: **Radioactive decay and half-life**

If you know how much of the radioactive isotope is present at the start of a given time as well as the half-life of the isotope, you can calculate how much will remain after a given period of time has elapsed using the nuclear decay equation given in section 1 of the *Chemistry Data Booklet*.

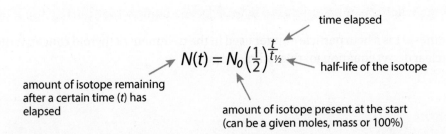

time elapsed

$$N(t) = N_0 \left(\frac{1}{2}\right)^{\frac{t}{t_{1/2}}}$$

half-life of the isotope

amount of isotope remaining after a certain time (t) has elapsed

amount of isotope present at the start (can be a given moles, mass or 100%)

You will need to make sure that you have practised how to use the y^x function on your calculator.

This formula will give the amount of the isotope remaining, so if you need to find the amount that has decayed, then you will need to subtract the remaining amount from the total starting amount.

The half-life of technetium-99m used in medical imaging is 6 hours. Calculate the percentage of the radioisotope remaining after 15 hours.

As a percentage is required, $N_0 = 100\%$

Percentage after 15 hours, $N(15) = 100 \left(\frac{1}{2}\right)^{15 \div 6} = 100 \left(\frac{1}{2}\right)^{2.5} = 100 \times 0.177 = 18\%$

Note that in medical use there might be less than the calculated percentage of the isotope left in the body, as the body may well excrete some of the radioisotope.

1. Iodine-131 is a beta particle emitter used in the treatment of thyroid cancer. Write the nuclear decay equation for this radioisotope. [2]

2. Outline *three* advantages of using technetium-99m as a radioactive tracer in nuclear medicine. [3]

3. Suggest and explain *two* advantages of targeted alpha therapy (TAT) over more common beta emitting isotopes in the treatment of cancer. [4]

4. Lutetium-177 has a half-life of 6.6 days. Calculate the mass that would have decayed after 2 weeks, if the initial dose was 5.00 mg [2]

Chapter 9:   Drug and Detection Analysis (HL only)

9.1   Alcohol detection using a 'breathalyser'

9.1.1   Alcohol detection using the dichromate breathalyser

The presence of alcohol in a sample of breath was originally detected through the use of the colour change from orange to green association with the oxidation of ethanol using **acidified potassium dichromate(VI).** In this reaction, ethanol is oxidised initially to ethanal and then to ethanoic acid. The changes of organic functional group can be represented by a simple equation, which does not include details of the oxidising agent.

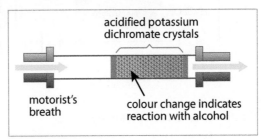

Figure 9.1: **A simple dichromate-based breathalyser**

$$\text{ethanol} \quad + \quad \text{oxidising agent} \quad \rightarrow \quad \text{ethanal} \quad + \quad \text{water}$$

$$C_2H_5OH \quad + \quad [O] \quad \rightarrow \quad CH_3CHO \quad + \quad H_2O$$

To explain the colour change, the full equation is needed. This can be constructed by combining the redox half equations for the oxidation of ethanol and the reduction of acidified dichromate(VI) ions (see core topic 9.1).

Oxidation: $(\quad C_2H_5OH \quad \rightarrow \quad CH_3CHO \quad + \quad 2H^+ \quad + \quad 2e^- \quad) \times \mathbf{3}$

$\uparrow$
Needed to balance the number of e^-
lost during oxidation with the
number gained during reduction

Reduction: $Cr_2O_7^{2-} \quad + \quad 14H^+ \quad + \quad 6e^- \quad \rightarrow \quad 2Cr^{3+} \quad + \quad 7H_2O$

Overall: $Cr_2O_7^{2-} \quad + \quad 8H^+ \quad + \quad 3C_2H_5OH \quad \rightarrow \quad 2Cr^{3+} \quad + \quad 7H_2O \quad 3CH_3CHO$
$\uparrow$
The overall number of H$^+$ ions is obtained by
subtracting the 6H$^+$ formed in the oxidation
from the 14H$^+$ needed by the reduction.

Combining redox half-equations into an overall equation for a redox reaction is introduced in core topic 9.1. Also, the oxidation of ethanol using potassium dichromate(VI) is met in core topic 10.2.

A similar equation can be constructed for the further oxidation of ethanal to ethanoic acid. In the breathalyser, the breath from the motorist is passed over crystals of orange potassium dichromate(VI). The presence of ethanol is indicated by the appearance of green colour due to the formation of the chromium(III) ions from the oxidation reactions.

9.1.2 Alcohol detection using the fuel cell breathalyser

The original portable breathalyser above has largely been replaced by a more precise instrument based on a **fuel cell**. This is a voltaic cell that generates a current as oxygen from air is used to oxidise the ethanol (see core topic 9.2). The ethanol is oxidised as above to give ethanal and then ethanoic acid. The half-equation for the reduction of oxygen is:

Reduction: $\quad O_2 + 4H^+ + 4e^- \rightarrow 2H_2O$

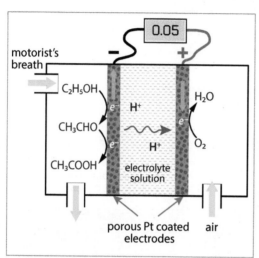

In the fuel cell, the ethanol in the breath is separated from oxygen in air by two platinum electrodes that are porous to allow H^+ ions to move through them. The two electrodes are then connected by a suitable electrolyte to allow the H^+ ions to pass from the anode to the cathode. The electrons produced are made to flow via an ammeter that measures the current. This current will depend on the concentration of ethanol in the sample of breath.

Figure 9.2: **A fuel cell breathalyser**

9.2 Analysis and identification of drug molecules using IR, ^{1}H NMR and mass spectrometry

The structures of drug molecules can be analysed and identified through the use of **infrared spectroscopy**, **mass spectroscopy**, and **proton NMR**. These techniques are used extensively during the development and use of drugs.

9.2.1 Steroid detection in sport

Anabolic steroids are synthetic hormones that mimic the action of testosterone to produce an increase in muscle mass. They are used medically to help patients recover from injury or starvation. They can also be used in bodybuilding to enhance strength or physique. The use of anabolic steroids to gain an advantage in competitive sports is banned by all major sporting bodies, including the International Olympic Committee. Therefore, rigorous testing of athletes is carried out to detect the presence of steroids in their urine or blood.

Steroids are lipids with a characteristic fused ring structure, known as a **steroidal backbone**. The structure of cholesterol is given in the section 34 of the *Chemistry Data Booklet*.

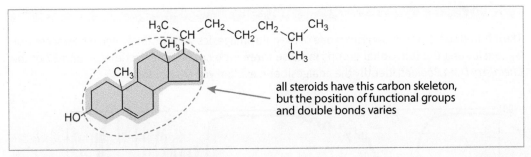

all steroids have this carbon skeleton, but the position of functional groups and double bonds varies

Figure 9.3: **The structure of cholesterol**

Gas or liquid **chromatography** is used to separate and identify mixtures containing steroids. In this technique, the mixture is injected into one end of a long tube containing a non-volatile liquid (the stationary phase) and carried along the tube by a carrier gas or liquid (the mobile phase) that flows through the tube at a steady rate. Different molecules have different affinities for the two phases and therefore come out of the tube at different times. A detector at the end of the tube records a peak on the chromatogram as each substance leaves the tube. The time between the injection and detection for each substance if known as its **retention time**. This can be compared to known values and used to suggest the identity of the steroid.

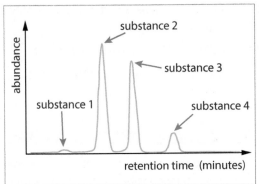

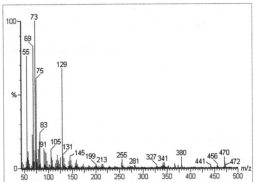

Figure 9.4: **Gas chromatogram of a mixture containing four substances of differing amounts**

Figure 9.5: **Mass spectrum of a steroid**

To improve the identification of steroids, gas chromatography is often combined with **mass spectroscopy**, by passing each of the separated substances into a mass spectrometer one by one as they come out of the tube. This combined technique is often abbreviated as GC-MS. The mass spectrum of a steroid will contain a large number of peaks due to the many different ways of fragmenting the large steroid molecule. The exact pattern of these fragment peaks will differ according to which particular steroid is being detected. This can be compared by the computer to a library of known compounds and allow identification of the particular steroid in the sample.

The infrared spectrum below is from one of the mild analgesics: aspirin, ibuprofen, or paracetamol. By considering the functional groups in these three molecules using sections 26 and 37 of the *Chemistry Data Booklet*, identify the analgesic and explain your reasoning.

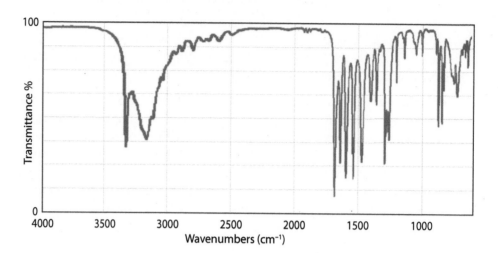

Aspirin contains ester and carboxyl groups; ibuprofen contains a carboxyl group only; paracetamol contains phenol and carboxamide groups.

The carboxyl group would produce a broad peak at 2500–3000 cm⁻¹, so it is not present.

Peaks at 3200 and 1700 cm⁻¹ are produced by the O–H of the phenol and the C=O of the carboxamide respectively, confirming that it is **paracetamol**.

The mass spectrum of omeprazole contains many fragment peaks. Use sections 28 and 37 of the *Chemistry Data Booklet* to suggest the identity of the fragments responsible for two peaks with a mass less than 50.

Of the fragments listed in section 28 of the *Chemistry Data Booklet*, those that occur in the structure are CH_3^+ ($m/z = 15$) and CH_3O^+ ($m/z = 31$).

The ¹H NMR spectrum of paracetamol (acetaminophen) shows two peaks, each of relative area 2 in the range 6.9–9.0 ppm. These two peaks are due to the four protons directly attached to the benzene ring.

(a) Use section 37 of the Chemistry Data Booklet to deduce the number of additional peaks that would be present on this 1H NMR spectrum and state their relative peak areas.

(b) Explain whether or not any of these additional peaks would be split.

The additional protons in the structure are –OH, –NH, and –CH3. Therefore, you would expect **three more peaks**, with relative peak areas: **1:1:3**.

Each of these groups is attached to a carbon that has no protons on it. Therefore, all three peaks would **not be split**.

9.3 Extraction and purification of an organic product

The development, production, and analysis of drugs often requires separation of the desired compound from other substances in the mixture. While chromatography is useful for small amounts for analysis, separation of larger quantities is usually based on the differing physical properties of the substances in the mixture. In particular:

- Differing boiling points—separated by **fractional distillation**
- Solubility in polar/non-polar solvents—separated by **solvent extraction**.

9.3.1 Fractional distillation

This method is used to separate homogenous mixtures of liquids with differing boiling points.

When the mixture of two liquids with different boiling points is heated, the mixture will boil at a temperature in between that of the two liquids. For example, a 50:50 by mass mixture of ethanol (b.p. 78°C) and water (b.p. 100°C) will boil at about 92°C. The vapour will contain both compounds, although it will be richer in the more volatile ethanol (see **Raoult's law**

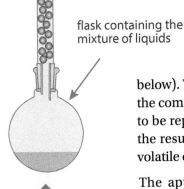

water in

water out

glass beads

the more volatile liquid collects here

flask containing the mixture of liquids

HEAT

Figure 9.6: **Laboratory apparatus for fractional distillation**

below). Therefore, simple distillation will not completely separate the compounds. To get a much better separation, the liquids need to be repeatedly boiled and condensed. Each time this happens, the resulting mixture contains a greater proportion of the more volatile component.

The apparatus is designed to allow the mixture to boil and condense many times, so it produces the purest possible product. The tube above the flask contains glass beads. This allows the vapour to pass upward but also provides a surface on which the vapour can condense and re-boil. By the time the vapour reaches the top, it will contain almost only the more volatile component, which is then condensed into a collecting tube. The less volatile component will drip back into the flask.

Raoult's law can be used to predict the boiling point of the mixture of liquids if the proportions of each component in the liquid mixture are known. The proportions are measured in terms of the mole fraction of each component: in other words, the amount of the one component divided by the total moles of all the components in the liquid mixture added together.

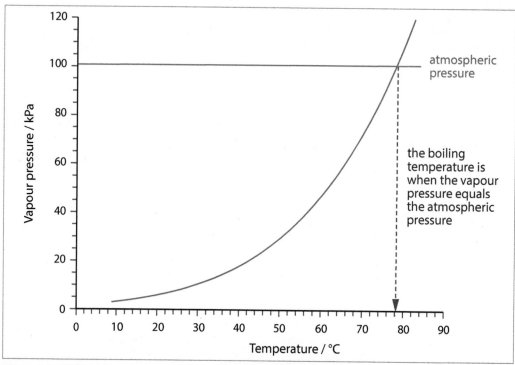

Figure 9.7: **Change in vapour pressure of ethanol with temperature**

You also need to know the **vapour pressure** (or technically, the *saturated* **vapour pressure**) of each component at the given temperature. The vapour pressure of a liquid effectively gives the concentration of the vapour above the surface of the liquid at a given temperature. The vapour pressure will increase as the temperature increases, until it reaches atmospheric pressure—at which point the liquid will boil.

For a mixture containing two substances, A and B, the Raoult's law can be applied as follows:

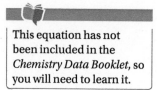

This equation has not been included in the *Chemistry Data Booklet,* so you will need to learn it.

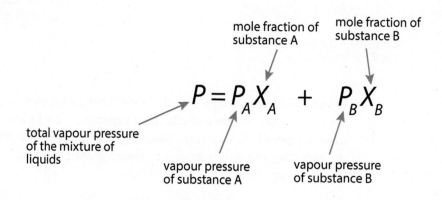

$$P = P_A X_A + P_B X_B$$

mole fraction of substance A

mole fraction of substance B

total vapour pressure of the mixture of liquids

vapour pressure of substance A

vapour pressure of substance B

A mixture contains 4.6 g of ethanol, added to 3.6 cm³ of distilled water. At 80°C, the vapour pressure of pure ethanol is 108.3 kPa, and the vapour pressure of pure water is 47.3 kPa. Calculate the vapour pressure of the mixture at this temperature.

Amount of ethanol $= 4.6\,g \div 46.08\,gmol^{-1} = 0.10\,mol$

Density of water $= 1.00\,gcm^{-3}$, so the amount of water $= 3.6\,g \div 18.02\,gmol^{-1} = 0.20\,mol$

Total moles $= 0.10 + 0.20 = 0.30\,mol$, so mole fractions are ethanol 0.33, and water 0.67

Vapour pressure of the mixture $= (108.3\,kPa \times 0.33) + (47.3\,kPa \times 0.67) = \mathbf{67.6\,kPa}$

You could be asked to suggest whether a particular drug molecule is likely to dissolve better in a polar or non-polar solvent, given its structure.

9.3.2 Solvent extraction

This method is used to separate an organic compound from a mixture by using its greater solubility in one particular solvent relative to another different solvent.

The mixture of organic compounds is added to a **separating funnel** that contains two immiscible solvents: for example, diethyl ether and water. The two solvents form two separate layers in the funnel, with the less dense liquid on the top. When shaken thoroughly, the organic compound will dissolve preferentially in one of the two layers depending on its structure. Ionic, highly polar and/or compounds containing O–H or N–H bonds will dissolve more readily in water, whereas non-polar compounds, such as hydrocarbons will dissolve more readily in the less polar solvent. This is because strong ion-dipole or hydrogen bonds can form between charged or polar solutes and water molecules. Non-polar solutes however will bond with the non-polar solvent using London (induced dipole/dispersion) forces.

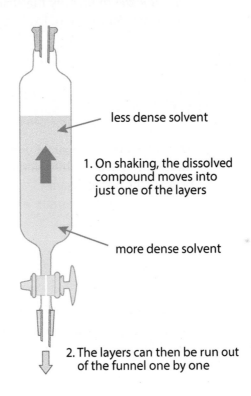

less dense solvent

1. On shaking, the dissolved compound moves into just one of the layers

more dense solvent

2. The layers can then be run out of the funnel one by one

Figure 9.8: **Solvent extraction using a separating funnel**

After shaking, the funnel is left for a few minutes to allow the layers to separate out again. Once the boundary between the two liquids is clearly visible, the lower layer is run off into a separate container, followed by the upper layer into a different container. The pure organic compound can then be recovered from the layer in which it has dissolved by gently evaporating off the solvent.

1. Outline how alcohol can be detected on the breath of a motorist using a fuel-cell breathalyser. [3]

....

....

....

....

2. Diamorphine (heroin) and morphine can be distinguished using a number of analytical techniques.

   (a) The NMR spectrum of diamorphine shows a peak with a chemical shift of 2.1 ppm that is not present in morphine. Use sections 27 and 37 of the *Chemistry Data Booklet* to identify the structural feature of the diamorphine molecule responsible for this peak. Explain your reasoning. [2]

   ....

   ....

   ....

   (b) The molecular ion peak of diamorphine has a higher m/z value than that of morphine. Calculate the difference between the m/z values of the molecular ion peaks of the two molecules. [2]

   ....

   ....

   ....

   (c) Use sections 26 and 37 of the *Chemistry Data Booklet* to identify the wavenumber range expected for any peaks that would be present in the infrared spectrum of morphine but would not be present in the infrared spectrum of diamorphine. [1]

   ....

   ....

   ....

3. 'Dianabol' is an anabolic steroid that is banned for athletes by all major sports bodies. Its structure is shown on the right.

   (a) Describe the structural feature that identifies this molecule as a steroid. [1]

....

....

(b) Outline how the presence of this compound or its metabolites can be detected in a sample of urine from the athlete. [4]

....

....

....

....

....

4. Some commercially available painkillers contain a mixture of paracetamol and caffeine. The caffeine can be separated using solvent extraction with a non-polar solvent such as dichloromethane. Use the structure of paracetamol given in section 37 of the *Chemistry Data Booklet* and the structure of caffeine shown here to explain why caffeine is more soluble in the non-polar solvent than paracetamol. [3]

....

....

....

....

Appendix: Answers to Revision Questions

Award one mark for each point ending in a semicolon. Alternative answers are indicated with a /.

Pharmaceutical Products and Drug Action (page 5)

1. From animal studies: $\dfrac{LD_{50}}{ED_{50}}$

   From human studies: $\dfrac{TD_{50}}{ED_{50}}$

   Testing is kept to a minimum because of: ethical concern over cruelty to animals; economic reasons/cost of testing.

2. Tolerance is when larger amounts of the drug is needed to have the original effect; addiction is when the patient becomes compulsive about taking the drug.

3. Bioavailability is the fraction of the administered dosage that reaches the target part of the human body.

   Two factors that affect bioavailability are:
   - the method of administration;   - the polarity of the drug;

   (Other factors include: formulation of the drug; taking with other drugs; taking with food; health of the patient).

4. Any five of:
   - identifying the need;   - in vitro testing;
   - identifying a possible structure   - testing on animals; testing on
     using computer simulation of   humans; extraction/synthesis on a
     binding;   large/commercial scale.

5. Hydrogen bonding; due to the OH/hydroxyl group; London/dispersion/induced dipole forces; due to the phenyl/propyl/hydrocarbon groups.

Aspirin and Penicillin (page 12)

1. Intercepts the pain stimulus at the source; by interfering with the production of substances that cause the pain, swelling or fever.

2. Add (an excess) of ethanoic anhydride to the salicylic acid (crystals); add (cold) deionised/distilled water to the mixture; filter the mixture (by vacuum filtration); recrystallize the solid in ethanol/other suitable solvent/or a description of the process of recrystallization); measure the melting point of the aspirin (which should be a sharp change at 138–140°C); record the IR spectrum of the aspirin (which should show only carboxyl and ester groups).

3. The combination of two drugs produces an effect that is greater than the sum of their individual effects; ethanol enhances the effect of aspirin to cause stomach bleeding.

4. (a)

(b) Ionic/charged/more polar COO– group gives greater solubility in water; more readily transported/more concentrated in the blood.

5. In both aspirin and penicillins: carboxyl.

In just aspirin: ester/phenyl (benzene ring).

6. React/interfere with the enzyme responsible for bacterial cell wall formation; the beta-lactam ring is strained/has smaller bond angles than the normal 109.5°; so it opens up easily/bonds are weaker.

7. Any four of:
   - bacteria can become resistant to the antibiotic;
   - due to a greater number of bacteria being exposed to the antibiotic, so a greater probability of resistance developing;
   - resistant bacteria have a penicillinase enzyme (that breaks down penicillins);
   - modification changes the shape of the molecule;
   - so, it does not bind to/fit into the active site of the penicillinase enzyme.

Opiates (page 16)

1. Any three of:
   - cross the blood-brain barrier;
   - binds to opioid receptor sites in the brain;
   - supressing the transmission of pain impulses;
   - their structure resembles natural painkillers produced by the body.

2. (a)

   Formula of suitable reagent: ethanoic acid, or ethanoic anhydride; correct balanced equation.

(b) Diamorphine contains ester groups instead of hydroxyl groups; diamorphine/ ester groups are less polar (than hydroxyl groups); diamorphine is more soluble in fat/lipid; diamorphine crosses the non-polar/lipid blood-brain barrier more quickly.

3. Disadvantages: any two of:

    – can lead to: addition/dependence/ withdrawal symptoms if stopped;
    – side effects of: sedation/ depression/apathy/reduction in breathing rate;

    – side effects of: constipation/nausea long-term use can lead to kidney failure/tolerance.

    Advantages: any two of:

    – fast effective pain relief;
    – wide therapeutic window;

    – relaxation/calming effect.

pH Regulation of the Stomach (page 21)

1. $CaCO_3 + 2HCl \rightarrow CaCl_2 + CO_2 + H_2O$

    Amount of NaOH needed to neutralise the remaining acid = vol. × conc. = $0.0252 \times 0.200 = 0.00504$ mol

    Equation ratio NaOH : HCl = 1:1, so amount of remaining HCl = 0.00504 mol

    Initial amount of acid = vol. × conc. = $0.100 \times 0.100 = 0.0100$ mol

    Amount of HCl that reacted with the tablet = 0.0100 – 0.00504 = 0.00496 mol

    Equation ratio $CaCO_3$: HCl = 1:2, so the amount of $CaCO_3$ in tablet = 0.00496 ÷ 2 = 0.00248 mol

    The M_r of $CaCO_3$ = 100.09, so the mass of $CaCO_3$ in tablet = 100.09 × 0.00248 = 0.248 g

    Total mass of two tablets = 2 × 200 mg = 0.400 g, so % purity = 0.248 ÷ 0.400 = 62.1%

2. Antacid: neutralises the excess acid, so raises pH. Advantage: quick acting.

    Ranitidine: inhibits the production of H^+ ions, so it raises the pH. Advantage: gives longer term relief.

3. A drug that is converted into a modified form by a metabolic process in the body.

    Omeprazole is supplied in an inactive form that is converted by a rearrangement reaction inside the cell to give the active form.

4. pK_a for benzoic acid = 4.20 and using the Henderson-Hasselbach equation, $pH = pK_a + \log [A^-]/[A]$;

    $4.0 = 4.20 + \log [A^-]/[A]$, so $\log [A^-]/[A] = -0.2$

    $[A^-]/[A] = 10^{-0.2} = 0.63$ hence 1.58 for $[C_6H_5COOH]/[C_6H_5COONa]$

Antiviral Medications (page 24)

1. Viruses:

    – are smaller;
    – need a host cell to reproduce;

    – are not living/DNA or RNA surrounded by protein/no cell wall, nucleus or cytoplasm.

    Viruses are difficult to target with drugs because:

    – they only reproduce inside living cells;

    – they mutate easily, leading to resistance.

2. Inhibits the enzyme neuraminidase; this prevents the new viruses leaving the host cell.

3. Any three of: (primary) amine; ether; alkenyl; carboxamide.

4. Mutation of protein coating the virus/produced by the virus within the host cell; viral protein no longer binds to/reacts with the drug molecule.

   To combat the problem of viral resistance, any two of:

   - monitoring of patient compliance, so that the full dose is taken to ensure no viruses survive;
   - don't use the drug as a prophylactic (preventative) treatment;
   - drugs have been developed that target more than one protein.

Environmental Impact of Some Medications (page 28)

1. Low-level waste: protective clothing/gloves/syringes/swabs tissues; store in shielded containers until the isotope has decayed then dispose as non-radioactive waste.

   Intermediate-level waste: radioisotopes/equipment; store in shielded/steel containers and bury in concrete chambers underground.

2. Any two of:
   - halogenated solvents can deplete the ozone layer;
   - solvents are non-biodegradable/ can accumulate in the environment;
   - solvents can be toxic to humans or animals.

3. The use of genetically modified E. coli bacteria to make shikimic acid: has fewer steps, so better yield and atom economy; can be done at lower temperatures; uses no toxic solvents.

Taxol: A Chiral Auxiliary Case Study (page 33)

1. Natural source: the (bark of the) Pacific Yew tree; the Pacific Yew is rare/could be endangered by harvesting; chemical synthesis can start with a compound from the common European Yew tree.

2. The chiral auxiliary: is added to the molecule at the start of the synthesis; prevents formation of other stereoisomers/enantiomers than the desired one; is then removed once the chiral centre(s) have formed.

3. (a) Polarised light is passed through the sample; the angle of rotation is measured by rotating a polarising filter beyond the sample until the emitted light passes through; the two enantiomers will rotate the light equally in opposite directions.

   (b) A racemic mixture will not rotate the polarised light both enantiomers are present in equal amounts, so their effects cancel out.

Nuclear Medicine (page 40)

1. $^{131}_{53}I \; > \; ^{131}_{54}Xe \; + \; ^{0}_{-1}e \;$ (or $^{0}_{-1}\beta$)

   Correct mass and atomic number for a β-particle; rest of the equation correct.

2. Any three of:
    - gamma rays are easily detected, so only small quantities of the isotope are needed;
    - gamma rays (in these small quantities) do not cause significant local damage to tissues;
    - short half-life lessens long term damage to tissues;
    - the product, technetium-99 is not very radioactive;
    - easily produced from uranium from nuclear reactors.

3. Antibodies can target only the tumour cells throughout the body (whereas beta emitters are not targeted as effectively); so, TAT will be effective against secondary cancers/less harmful to other tissues; alpha-particles have a higher energy and shorter path length than beta-particles; so are very effective in killing surrounding cells, but not other nearby tissue.

4. Use of: $N(t) = N_0\left(\frac{1}{2}\right)^{\frac{t}{t_{\frac{1}{2}}}}$ and 2 weeks = 14 days

    So, the amount remaining after 14 days = $5.00\left(\frac{1}{2}\right)^{\frac{14}{6.6}} = 1.15\,\text{mg}$

    Therefore, the mass that decayed = $5.00 - 1.15 = 3.85\,\text{mg}$

Drug Detection and Analysis (page 48)

1. Any three of:
    - ethanol is separated from oxygen with two porous Pt electrodes and electrolyte in between;
    - H^+ ions (lost from oxidation of ethanol) move between the electrodes;
    - electrons/electric current flow (between the electrodes) via an ammeter to measure current;
    - oxygen (from air) is reduced by the electrons and H^+ ions.

2. (a.) Peak at 2.1 ppm is due to CH_3COOR/ester; ester/carbonyl group is not present in morphine.

    (b.) Diamorphine has $2 \times CH_3COO^-$ instead of $2 \times -OH$ in morphine; diamorphine would have M_r higher by $2 \times (24+3+32) - 2 \times (16+1) = 84$

    (c.) Morphine has OH in alcohol/phenol with peak(s) at 3200–3600 cm^{-1}

3. (a.) Four fused rings with three hexagons/6-carbon and one pentagon/5-carbon

    (b.) Any four of:
    - using GC-MS;
    - GC separates the steroid from other substances in the urine;
    - by vapourising the mixture and using a carrier gas to pass it through a long column;
    - (peak at) the retention time is characteristic of the particular compound;
    - (pattern of fragments in the) mass spectrum of the compound is unique/can be compared to a library of known compounds.

4. Any three of:
    - paracetamol contains polar OH and NH groups, but caffeine is less polar/does not contain OH and NH;
    - paracetamol can/caffeine cannot form (strong) hydrogen bonds;
    - caffeine is a larger molecule, with more electrons;
    - so, it forms stronger London forces with the non-polar solvent.